This book belongs to

• •

CLASSIC
TALES OF INDIA
For Children

CONTENTS

6

INTRODUCTION

This book is a collection of short stories from the Indian classics. The book includes stories from the great Indian epics of the *Ramayan* and the *Mahabharat*, stories of *Akbar* and *Birbal* and animal stories from the *Panchatantra*, which children love to read, besides many others.

There are stories of wit, humour, love, betrayal, pride and courage, explained in a simple and interesting manner. Every story is complimented with beautiful illustrations which fascinate children. The stories are concluded with appropriate morals to impart wisdom to children and to help face day to day challenges of life.

It is hoped that the book will not only entertain children but also inculcate in them good values and worldly wisdom.

TRUE FRIENDS

In a forest, there lived four friends. One of them was a small, brown mouse. The second friend was a black crow. The other two friends were the deer and the tortoise. The four of them were very fond of each other and spent all their time together.

One day, the four of them decided to meet beside the lake. The mouse, the crow and the tortoise came but there was no sign of the deer. The three friends waited for sometime but the deer did not come.

"The deer is never late," said the mouse. "He runs very fast and always reaches before us. What could have happened today?"

"Perhaps, he is in some danger," said the crow.

"We should go and find out about our friend," said the tortoise. "I will fly over the forest and see if I can find him," said the crow.

So, the crow flew at once and started looking for the deer.

After sometime, when he had flown a little distance he saw the deer trapped in a net. The crow flew down and went close to the deer. "Oh, you are trapped in a hunter's net," said the mouse. "Do not worry my friend. I shall go back and get help."

"Please get some help quickly," answered the deer crying softly.

The crow flew back to his friends and told them the whole story.

On hearing this, the tortoise said, "The mouse can cut the net with his teeth and rescue our friend."

"But how do I get there quickly?" asked the mouse.

"I can carry you on my back and we can fly there together," said the crow.

So, the crow flew away carrying the mouse on his back. Soon, they reached the place where the deer was.

The mouse immediately started cutting the net with his sharp teeth and soon the deer was free. By then, the tortoise had also reached there, crawling slowly all the way. The four friends were together again and started talking.

Suddenly, they heard the sound of footsteps and at once realized that the hunter was coming. At once, the crow flew to the top of a tall tree. The deer ran away and the mouse hid himself in a hole. The poor tortoise could not move quickly. Slowly, he walked towards a big green bush.

The hunter came and saw that the deer had escaped.

"Oh, what bad luck. Now what will I have for dinner?" said the hunter. Just then he saw the tortoise crawling towards the bush.

"Ha, Ha, you will be my dinner," said the hunter. He quickly grabbed the tortoise, put him in his bag and started walking home.

The crow, who was sitting on the tree saw this and called out to his friends, "Oh mouse! Oh deer! Please come quickly. Our friend, the tortoise is in danger."

The deer and the mouse came running to the crow. The crow told them how the hunter had carried away the tortoise in his bag.

"We must do something before the hunter gets home," said the crow.

"I have a plan," said the deer." Then he told his plan to the crow and the tortoise. They all agreed and went away.

The hunter was walking home carrying the tortoise in his bag. Suddenly, he saw the deer in front of him eating the grass.

"A deer, what luck?" said the hunter.

The hunter dropped the bag and ran after the deer to catch him.

When the hunter was out of sight, the mouse cut open the bag with his teeth. The tortoise got out of the bag and hid under a bush.

The hunter ran for sometime after the deer and then got tired. He stopped running and returned to collect his bag. When the hunter found his bag empty, he was shocked.

"What, no tortoise?" cried the hunter. "But how could he escape?"

"I am very unlucky," the hunter said sadly. "First the deer got away and now even this slow tortoise has escaped. I will have to sleep hungry tonight!"

The tortoise, the mouse, the crow and the deer smiled as they quietly watched the hunter going away.

A Friend in Need is a Friend Indeed

HOW GANESH BECAME GANPATI?

Goddess Parvati, wife of God Shiv, was going for a bath. So she instructed her husband God Shiv's bull, Nandi, to guard the entrance to the palace.

"Do not let anyone enter this chamber while I am taking a bath," said Parvati to Nandi. "I do not like anyone intruding upon my privacy."

"Yes, madam," answered Nandi.

But when God Shiv came, Nandi could not stop him. When Parvati saw Shiv in her chamber, she was very annoyed.

"I will create my own guard," said Parvati to herself.

Parvati rubbed her body with jasmine oil and sandal paste. Then, she scraped off some of the scented paste from her body. She mixed the scented paste with water and clay from the river Ganga and made a clay boy from it. Holding the clay child close to her lips, Parvati infused life into him. The next moment, the clay child became a handsome young boy and looked at his mother with wondering eyes. Parvati embraced her son and named him Ganesh.

"My son, you shall be my guard," Parvati said. "Do not let anyone enter this chamber while I am taking a bath."

"Yes, mother," answered Ganesh.

Ganesh stood outside the door of the chamber with his sturdy young legs firmly apart. Parvati went in for a long, leisurely bath.

When Shiv returned to Kailash, he was surprised to find a young boy standing outside Parvati's chamber. Without bothering to talk to him, Shiv approached the door to enter inside the chamber. Ganesh blocked Shiv's path and stopped him from entering the chamber.

Shiv became angry and said, "Step aside, boy. I wish to enter."

"You cannot go in," said Ganesh.

Shiv lost his temper on hearing this and told Ganesh to let him enter if he valued his life. But Ganesh did not budge.

"You cannot go in," Ganesh repeated. "My mother said not to let anyone enter the chamber."

"I don't care what your mother said. Get out of my way before I destroy you," Shiv shouted angrily. But Ganesh still did not move away. Then, Shiv ordered his *ganas* (assistants) to destroy Ganesh. The *ganas* fought with Ganesh but they were no match for him. Ganesh easily defeated all of them.

Then, Shiv sent god Brahma, the god of creation, in the disguise of a sage (saadhu) to talk to Ganesh. Brahma tried to persuade Ganesh to let Shiv enter. But Ganesh did not listen to him and made matters worse by pulling at his beard.

Then, it was god Vishnu's turn to fight Ganesh. During the fight, for a moment, Ganesh came to be unarmed and Shiv chopped his head from behind. As Shiv's trident (trishul) touched Ganesh's neck, he cried out "Mother!".

Hearing the loud cry, Parvati came out running only to see Ganesh's head roll away and lie still. Hot, angry tears streamed down Parvati's cheeks.

"You cruel brute, what have you done?" Parvati said angrily to Shiv. "You killed my son. How could you? I will never forgive you and the devas (other gods) for this."

"I did not know he was your son. Please forgive me," Shiv apologized to Parvati, already repenting his action. But Parvati was much too angry and hurt to forgive. She ordered her destructive manifestations Goddesses Durga and Kali to destroy the *devas*. The *devas* fell at Parvati's feet and begged forgiveness.

"I can only forgive you if you restore my son's life," cried out Parvati.

Shiv sent his *ganas* to bring the head of the first living thing they see. The *ganas* went out of Kailash and the first thing they saw was an elephant. They cut its head off and gave it to Shiv. Shiv placed the head on Ganesh's raw, bleeding neck. The head joined seamlessly and Ganesh opened his eyes.

Shiv raised his son and embraced him. He blessed him saying "You, my son, will be the leader of my *ganas* and so will be know as *Ganpati*. You shall be the first to be worshipped amongst Gods and no God or man will begin any venture without first making offerings to you. In you shall lie the power to remove all obstacles from the path of men."

After blessing Ganesh, Shiv turned to Parvati and said, "Are you happy now?"

Parvati gave him an approving smile and entered her chamber with Ganesh.

THE UNCOOKED RICE

Akbar, the emperor of India, was a great ruler. Akbar enjoyed culture and the arts and always kept himself surrounded with intelligent and learned people. There were nine men whom he was especially fond of and called them his *Navratnas* or nine gems. And of the nine gems, the most intelligent was Birbal.

Birbal was Akbar's favourite courtier and that made the other people in the court jealous. The other courtiers were always plotting against Birbal.

But, Birbal, with his incomparable wit, always defeated his enemies.

One day, Akbar was in his court, as usual surrounded by wise men. Akbar loved discussions and put forward a question to carry out his favourite pass time. Akbar said, "Once a wise man said that people will do anything for money. But I believe that there are certain things that nobody will do even if I were to offer a great reward."

A hush fell over the court and all the courtiers listened carefully to Akbar's words.

"There is a lake opposite the palace gardens," Akbar said. "No one would dare to stand in that ice cold water for a whole night, with nothing to warm himself, even if I would offer a great reward for doing so."

Everyone in the court agreed with what Akbar said, except Birbal.

"I wish I could agree with you, your majesty," Birbal said, "but, probably if I try, I can find a man who would stand in the lake and win the reward."

"In that case, Birbal," said Akbar, "you find such a man and I will give him a thousand gold coins."

The next day, Birbal brought a woodcutter to Akbar's court who was willing to stand in the lake to win the reward.

The emperor asked the woodcutter, "Why are you putting your life at risk?"

"I am a poor man, your majesty," answered the woodcutter, "and I need money to feed my hungry children and wife. If by taking this risk, I am able to feed my family, then I am ready for it."

"Alright then. Guards, take this woodcutter to the lake," ordered Akbar.

Two guards, as witnesses, went with the woodcutter. The woodcutter stepped into the ice cold water of the lake and stood there chest deep into the water. The whole night the woodcutter stood in the cold water shaking fiercely. At sunrise, he stepped out of the water.

"I have done it!" exclaimed the woodcutter still shaking fiercely, "Take me to the emperor. He will give me my reward."

The woodcutter went with the guards to the emperor's palace, "Your majesty," said the woodcutter, "I have completed the task. I stood in the lake all night for which your guards stand as witnesses. Please, give me my reward."

Akbar was surprised, at the same time impressed with the woodcutter. To reward the woodcutter, he decided to give him a thousand gold coins. As Akbar called for the coins, another courtier, Abdul Rahman, saw this as an opportunity to impress the emperor and be one up on Birbal.

"How did you manage to spend the whole night in ice cold water?" asked Abdul Rahman.

"Because of my need and determination, sir," answered the woodcutter.

"And what were you doing when your naked body was in the freezing water?" questioned Abdul Rahman.

"I looked at the palace lights glowing in the dark," answered the woodcutter.

"Then, you cheated," said Abdul Rahman. "The reward was for the person who would spend the night without having anything to warm himself. You derived warmth from the palace lights. Thus, you don't deserve the reward."

Akbar agreed with what Abdul Rahman said and the poor woodcutter was not given the reward. The woodcutter sadly went home.

After a few days, Birbal invited Akbar and Abdul Rahman for dinner to his house. Akbar and Abdul Rahman waited for a long time but no dinner was served. At last, Akbar grew tired of waiting and said, "Why are you not serving us dinner, Birbal? We are hungry."

"Sorry for the delay, your majesty. But the rice is taking a long time to cook," Birbal replied politely.

"It is only a little rice. Why is it taking so long to cook?" asked Akbar getting irritated.

"Why don't we go and see how it is coming along?" suggested Birbal. Birbal took his guests to a courtyard where a pot was tied to a high tree branch. Underneath the pot, a small fire was burning on the ground.

Birbal fanned the fire, as if trying to speed up the cooking.

"What is this stupidity?" asked Abdul Rahman. "This rice can never be cooked. How can the heat of this fire reach the pot so far away?"

"It is not that far," Birbal replied politely. "If the woodcutter can be warmed by looking at the palace lights a mile away, then this rice can surely be cooked with the heat of the fire which is closer to the rice."

"I have learnt my lesson, Birbal," Akbar said smiling. "Tomorrow morning, the woodcutter will be given his reward twice over."

Appreciate People Instead of Finding Faults

CROWS AND THE SNAKE

A male crow and a female crow lived in their nest on a tree. They had many children and the family lived together happily.

One day, a large black snake came and made its hole under the same tree. The mother crow saw this and said to the father crow, "This large snake has come to live under this tree. With him around, I am worried for our children's safety."

The father crow said, "You are right, but what can we do about it. We cannot

stop the snake from living here." One day, while the crows had gone to search for food, the snake crawled up the tree and ate the baby crows. When the father and the mother crow came back, they were shocked to find their children missing. They looked everywhere but could not find their children.

They cried a lot and decided to keep a better watch when they had children again. After a few months, the mother crow laid some eggs. The eggs hatched and they had children again.

"We should be careful this time," said the father crow. "We should never leave our children alone. One of us should go out to get food and the other should always stay at home with the children."

One day, when the father crow had gone out to get food, the mother crow saw the snake coming up the tree. She cried for help and tried to drive away the snake. But the snake came up on the tree and ate the baby crows.

The snake then went into its hole.

When the father crow returned, he found the mother crow crying. When he found out what had happened, he was also very sad.

"Let us leave this place," said the mother crow. "As long as this wicked snake lives here, we are not safe."

"Why should we leave?" said the father crow. "We have been living here for so many years. It is this wicked snake who has to leave."

"But who will drive him away?" asked the mother crow.

"We will go and meet our friend, the fox. He is clever. He will help us," said the father crow.

The crows went to the fox and told him what had happened. The fox thought for a while and then said, "I know how we can get rid of this snake. Do as I tell you and the snake will be killed."

"We will do as you say, but please, save us from this wicked snake," cried out both the crows. The fox said, "Tomorrow morning the ladies of the king's palace will go to the river for their bath. They will remove their ornaments and clothes and keep it on the river bank before entering the water. Their servants will be standing at a distance keeping a watch on the valuables. When nobody is near, one of you pick up a necklace and fly away. Make a lot of noise as you are flying so that the servants see you. They will run after you to get the necklace back. You fly straight to your tree and drop the necklace into the snake's hole."

The crows agreed to follow the fox's plan. The next morning they went to the river. As soon as the ladies kept their ornaments and clothes on the river bank and entered the water, the mother crow picked up a necklace and flew away.

The father crow followed her, cawing loudly to attract the attention of the servants. One of the servants saw the crow flying with the necklace and said, "That is a very valuable necklace that the crow is carrying. Let us get it back or the madam will be angry."

The servants followed the crows and saw the mother crow dropping the necklace into the snake's hole.

"Let us use a long stick to take out the necklace from the hole," one of the servants said. When the stick was put inside the hole, the snake felt disturbed and came out hissing. The servants saw the snake and pierced their spears into it. The snake died and they took out the necklace from the hole.

The crows were happy that the snake was dead.

A Powerful Enemy can be Defeated by Using Intelligence and Courage

SECRET MANTRA

Long, long ago, the world was divided between two category of people- the *Devas* (gods) and the *Asuras* (demons). The *Devas* and the *Asuras* were always fighting each other for power and supremacy. During the frequent wars between the *Devas* and the *Asuras*, the *Asuras* had an advantage- their guru Sukracharya knew the *mantra* (secret formula) of bringing the dead back to life. When the *Devas* died in battle, they remained dead but the dead *Asuras* were brought back to life by their guru Sukracharya. Sukracharya was the only one who knew the secret *mantra* and the *Asuras* took full advantage of this. The *Asuras* made war whenever they felt like. The *Devas* did not have anyone who knew the art of reviving the dead. They went to their guru Brihaspati for advice.

Brihaspati said, "Only Sukracharya knows the mantra of bringing the dead back to life. Someone from your side should go and stay with him as his student and acquire that knowledge." The gods thought for a while and then said, "The only person who is capable of undertaking such a difficult task is your own son, Kacha. He is kind and pure hearted and does nothing for personal gain."

Brihaspati approved of the gods' choice and called for his son.

"Go to Sukracharya and study under him as his student," said Brihaspati to Kacha. "Learn the art of bringing the dead back to life from him. Serve him with devotion and obey him in all things."

Kacha did not like the idea of living with the demons, but he agreed to do as was told without arguing. He respected his father and could not say no to him. " I will do my best to learn the art," said Kacha respectfully. He took leave of the *Devas* and went to the city of *Asuras*. He walked through the city and soon reached Sukracharya's hermitage.

"O Great sage," said Kacha to Sukracharya, "I am Kacha, son of Brihaspati. I want to gain knowledge from you. Please accept me as your student."

Kacha neither hid his identity nor the purpose of his visit. Sukracharya liked his honesty and said, "You are welcome here, Kacha. But I am surprised that you have come to learn from me. What can I teach you that your father cannot? Anyway, I shall try and help you in whatever way I can."

Sukracharya knew that Kacha had come to learn the *mantra* for reviving the dead from him but he still accepted him as his student.

Sukracharya had a beautiful daughter named Devyani whom he loved very much. When Devyani saw the handsome Kacha, she instantly fell in love with him.

"Devyani," said Sukracharya, "this is Kacha. He will be staying with us till he completes his studies."

Kacha was a devoted student and studied meticulously under Sukracharya. In due course of time, Kacha and Devyani became friends. Although Devyani loved Kacha right from the start, Kacha did not respond to her love and considered her as a friend only. Kacha would help Devyani in her household chores and collect fruits and flowers for her. Sometimes, they would even sing and dance together.

The *Asuras* knew why Kacha was living in their city and were furious with Sukracharya for accepting him as his student. But they dare not voice their complaint as they feared their guru might feel offended. The *Asuras* thought that if Kacha continued with his studies, he would soon learn the secret *mantra*. They decided they had to put a stop to it and the only way to do it was to kill Kacha. "We must kill Kacha," said the *Asuras*.

Kacha spent many years with Sukrachraya but Sukracharya did not teach him the *mantra* of reviving the dead. Kacha never pressed his guru to teach him nor did Sukracharya show any inclination to do so. But the *Asuras* did not know this and they made a plan to kill Kacha.

One day, when Kacha had taken his guru's cows to graze in the jungle, the *Asuras* surrounded him and killed him. Then they cut his body into little pieces and fed it to a wolf.

In the evening, Devyani was waiting for Kacha but the cows returned home without him. Devyani immediately realised that something terrible had happened to Kacha. Devyani started crying and ran straight to her father.

"O Father," cried out Devyani, "the sun has set, the cows have returned home and yet Kacha has not come. Bring him back. I cannot live without him."

Sukracharya consoled her saying, "Do not worry, child. I will bring Kacha back."

Using his powers, Sukracharya came to know that Kacha was dead. Sukracharya said his secret *mantra* silently and at once Kacha appeared before him. Devyani's joy knew no bounds as she saw Kacha fine and whole as he had ever been. "What happened to you?" asked Devyani anxiously.

"The *Asuras* killed me, cut my body into little pieces and fed the pieces to a wolf. When your father, the great Sukracharya, said his magic *mantra*, I came out tearing the wolf's body."

Sukracharya had made his daughter happy by reviving Kacha. But the *Asuras* were upset at their failure. The *Asuras* put their failure behind them and made another attempt at Kacha's life.

One day, Kacha was in the jungle collecting flowers when the *Asuras* caught him. They killed him and grinding his body into a paste, mixed it with the waters of the ocean.

In the evening, when Kacha did not return, Sukracharya and Devyani realized that the worst had happened. Devyani again pleaded to her father for Kacha's life. Sukracharya used the *mantra* again and brought Kacha back.

The *Asuras* were very angry that their guru had once more brought Kacha back to life.

"We must kill Kacha in a way that Sukracharya cannot revive him," said the *Asuras*. Then they made a very devious plan.

The *Asuras* caught Kacha a third time and killed him. They burnt his body and collected the ashes. Then, they dissolved the ashes in a jar of wine. Carrying the jar of wine, the *Asuras* went to Sukracharya and said, "We have brought you this delicious wine. Please accept it as a gesture of our respect for you."

Sukracharya liked wine and thanked the Asuras for it. The *Asuras*, with a sly smile on their faces, watched their guru drinking the wine.

In the evening, when Kacha did not return, Devyani went to her father. "The *Asuras* must have killed him again, father," Devyani cried out. "Bring him back."

But this time the problem was more serious than Devyani thought. Sukracharya realized at once that Kacha was in his stomach. Sukracharya said to Devyani, "My child, much as I want, I cannot revive Kacha this time."

But Devyani said, "If Kacha is dead, then I too will kill myself."

"Try to understand, Devyani," said Sukracharya, "Kacha is inside my stomach. If I revive Kacha, I would die."

"I cannot live without either of you," cried out Devyani. "Do something, father."

Sukracharya could not *see* Devyani's tears and decided to do something he would have never done otherwise. Sukracharya knew there was only one way out- he would have to teach Kacha the secret *mantra*.

Sukracharya taught the *mantra* to Kacha who was now inside his stomach. Kacha easily absorbed the magic *mantra* from his guru. Then, Sukracharya

recited the *mantra* and Kacha burst out of his stomach. As Kacha came out, Sukracharya fell dead. Kacha immediately revived his guru with his newly learnt *mantra*.

Sukracharya immediately got up and Kacha paid homage to him, calling him father as he was now born out of him. Sukracharya was very proud of Kacha for learning the *mantra* quickly. But he was also extremely angry with the *Asuras* for forcing him to teach Kacha the secret *mantra*.

Sukracharya went to the *Asuras* and said, "You stupid people. Your stupid actions left me with no choice but to teach Kacha the mantra of reviving the dead. Had you left him alone, he would have never learnt the *mantra*. You all are fools and I was a greater fool for drinking that wine. Therefore, no seeker of knowledge may drink wine."

Kacha stayed for some more time with Sukracharya and then decided to return to heaven. Kacha took leave of Sukracharya and thanked him for everything. Then, he went to Devyani to say goodbye to her.

"I have to return home" said Kacha to Devyani.

Tears fell from Devyani's eyes on hearing these words. "If you are leaving, marry me and take me with you. I have always loved you."

"How can I do that?" asked Kacha, "That would be a sin. I am your father's son now. You are my sister."

Devyani was heartbroken and cursed Kacha saying, "I curse you that you will never be able to practice what you have learnt. You will never be able to revive the dead."

Kacha said angrily, "Your curse is unjust. Take it back." But Devyani refused to do so.

Then Kacha said, "Your curse cannot stop me from teaching the *mantra*. I will teach it to others and so indirectly I will revive the dead. You said that what I have learnt will be useless but I will teach someone else and make it useful."

Kacha returned to heaven and the gods were pleased that he was successful in his mission.

THE BRAHMIN'S GOAT

Once, a Brahmin received a goat as a gift from his friend. The Brahmin thanked his friend for the gift and started walking back home. The little goat started acting naughty and pranced about darting here and there in the forest. The Brahmin tired of chasing it decided to carry it on his shoulders. Then, carrying the goat, the brahmin started walking home.

Three thieves saw the brahmin carrying the goat. One of them said, "That goat will make a good dinner for us. Let us steal it?"

The second thief said, "I have a plan." Then he told his plan to the other two. The three of them agreed and went away.

After a while, one of the thieves walked up to the brahmin and said, "Holy brahmin, why are you carrying a dog on your shoulders? It is not proper for a brahmin to carry a dog."

The brahmin became surprised on hearing this. "Dog, what dog?" he said angrily. "Are you blind? I am carrying a goat."

"Please don't be angry with me, sir. I am only telling you what I see. I am sorry if I bothered you." Saying this, the thief went away.

The brahmin continued walking. After he had gone a little further, the second thief came up to him. He looked at the brahmin and the goat and said, "Sir, why are you carrying a dead calf on your shoulders? It is shameful for a brahmin to carry a dead animal."

"Dead animal? What are you talking?" the brahmin shouted. "This is a live goat. I have just received this as a gift from my friend."

"Please don't get angry," said the thief. "If you wish to carry a dead calf, then do so. I will not say anything. Do as you please."

Now the brahmin became worried. He continued to walk but from time to time he looked at the animal.

"I wonder why those two men said all that. It is a goat and a live one at that," the brahmin said to himself.

Soon, he met the third thief. "Sorry to tell you, but what you are doing is not proper," said the thief. "A brahmin should never carry a donkey. In fact you should not even touch such an animal."

The brahmin became very confused. This was the third man he had met. And each of them had seen the goat as something else. The first one saw it as a dog, the second as a dead calf and the third as a donkey.

"Is this goat a monster or a demon that can change into something else every few minutes?" the brahmin thought to himself. "Perhaps, these men were telling the truth."

The brahmin became frightened and immediately threw the goat down. Then he ran home as fast as he could.

The third thief picked up the goat and hurried back to his friends. The thieves were happy that their plan was successful.

Never Trust the Words Spoken by Strangers

BHISHMA'S PROMISE

Long, long ago, there was a sage (*saadhu*) called Vasishta. He had a cow named Nandini whom he loved very much. The sage lived happily on the earth with his cow.

In heaven, there were eight gods who were known as the Vasu brothers. The Vasu brothers had everything they could desire but they still craved for more possessions. One day, they decided to steal sage Vasishta's cow. But, when the moment came, the seven older brothers got scared. However, the youngest brother, Prabhasa, stole the cow. Then, the brothers together hid the cow. When sage Vasishta found the cow missing, he was very angry. Using his supernatural powers, he came to know that the Vasu brothers were responsible for this.

Vasishta cursed them saying, "You brothers will have to be born on earth and live like ordinary human beings."

The Vasu brothers felt scared when they heard this and fell at Vasishta's feet to beg for forgiveness. Vasishta felt sorry for the Vasu brothers and said, "I cannot take away my curse. But I can soften it so it is easier for you to bear."

He told them that the seven older brothers would have a short life on earth, for only a few hours. But, Prabhasa, the youngest one, must spend one complete lifetime on earth as a human being. Prabhasa started crying on hearing this, but Vasishta consoled him saying that he would be an extraordinary human being.

Then, the Vasu brothers went to Goddess Ganga for help. "Help us, O Goddess! Come down to earth and we shall take birth from your womb. After our birth, put an end to our lives immediately so that we may return to heaven."

Goddess Ganga agreed to help them. Ganga came down to earth in the form of a beautiful woman. One day, king Shantanu of Hastinapur, saw a beautiful woman near the banks of the river Ganga. This woman was none other than Goddess Ganga herself. The king was so charmed by her beauty that he went upto her and proposed marriage.

"O beautiful maiden", Shantanu said, "I have never seen anyone as pretty as you. Marry me and become my queen."

"I can marry you," said Ganga "but only if you agree to my conditions."

"And what are they?" asked Shantanu impatiently.

"You must promise never to speak harshly to me or question my actions, whether good or evil," said Ganga.

The conditions were strange but Shantanu was so infatuated that he agreed. They married and soon a son was born to them. Shantanu was very happy but to his great sorrow, his beautiful wife threw the son into the river Ganga. The child died and Shantanu was very grieved. But Shantanu remembered his promise and did not say anything to his wife. Later, another son was born to them and he too was thrown into the river. After that, five more sons were born who met with the same cruel end.

When the eighth son was born, Shantanu lost his patience. When his wife was about to throw the child into the river, Shantanu stopped her and shouted, "Are you an evil demoness in human guise? You have killed seven children in cold blood. But I will not let you kill this one."

On hearing these words, his wife gave him a strange smile and said, "You have broken your promise, Shantanu! You have questioned my actions. Now I cannot stay with you."

Shantanu got scared on hearing this. Seeing his distress, Ganga told him her story. She told him that the seven children she threw into the river were the Vasu brothers, who by a curse had to be born on earth. But they desired to be released from this life as soon as they were born. Thus, she ended their lives and they went to heaven. The eighth child was cursed to a long life on earth.

"Now, that my work over I shall return to heaven taking the child with me as he is too young to be left without a mother" Ganga said. "But, one day," Ganga continued, "when your son is older, he would return to rightfully claim his father's throne."

Thus, Ganga left Shantanu taking the child with her. Several years went by. One day, Shantanu was walking along the banks of the river Ganga when he saw a very handsome boy. He was playing with the mighty waters of the river like a child playing with a loving mother. Just then, Goddess Ganga appeared before Shantanu and said, "O king, this is your eighth son. His name is Devrata. He is a very skilled archer and has learnt fighting skills from Parashuram. He has learnt the Vedas from Vasishta. He is fit to be your heir. Take him with you now."

King Shantanu took Devrata to his palace and crowned him the *Yuvraj* (the grand prince or the king in waiting).

After some time, Shantanu met a young fisherwoman with whom he fell in love instantly. Shantanu decided to marry her and met the fisherwoman's father.

"I want to marry your daughter," said Shantanu to the fisherman.

"I would be happy to accept your proposal but there is one condition," said the fisherman.

"And what is that?" asked Shantanu.

"My daughter Satyavati's children will inherit your throne," said the fisherman.

"But how is it possible? Devrata is my *Yuvraj*," cried out Shantanu.

"Then, the marriage is not possible. Nothing less than the throne for my daughter and her descendants is acceptable," concluded the fisherman.

Shantanu felt sad on hearing this and returned to his palace. Devrata saw his father looking sad and became anxious to know what had caused this. He loved his father very much and could not bear to see him sad. He asked the king's attendant and soon discovered the cause of his father's grief.

Then, Devrata went himself and met the fisherman. The fisherman told Devrata that Shantanu had refused to fulfil his condition for the marriage.

"What is the condition?" questioned Devrata.

"I want my daughter Satyavati's son to succeed Shantanu as the king," the fisherman answered.

"But, the king could have fulfilled this condition?" asked Devrata.

"How can he give away the throne without your consent? The throne is yours by right. Would you give up the throne for your father's happiness?" asked the fisherman mockingly.

"I don't care for the throne," said Devrata. "I will gladly give up the throne if it will make my father happy." The fisherman heard what Devrata had said but be was doubtful.

"I shall give up my claim on the throne and Satyavati's children shall rule after king Shantanu," said Devrata.

But, the fisherman was still not satisfied.

Then, Devrata turned his back to the fisherman and said in a firm voice, "I promise that I will never marry. My dynasty shall end with me."

As the young Devrata took this oath, the Gods in the heaven showered flowers on him and cried out, "Bhishma" to honour his selfless act. And after this, Devrata was forever known as *Bhishma* or the one who makes and keeps a great promise.

When Shantanu came to know of his son's great sacrifice, he embraced him and blessed him saying, "Live forever, Bhishma. You will never be defeated in battle and will be so strong that death shall not come to you, unless you desire it."

Make Your Parents Happy and Get Their Blessings

SAVITRI & THE GOD OF DEATH

Once upon a time, there lived a wise and powerful king, Ashvapati. He was extremely wealthy and had every luxury one could want. But he had one great sorrow. Even after years of marriage, he had no children. Though, the king was getting old, he was getting more determined to have a son. So, one day, the king decided to go to the forest and pray to Goddess Savitri (sister of the Sun God) to fulfil his desire.

After years of hard penance and prayers, Goddess Savitri appeared before the old king and said, "I am pleased with you. Ask what you want?"

The king with folded hands, politely said, "I want sons for my life has lost meaning without them."

"You shall not have sons," the Goddess said, "but you shall have a daughter of immense wisdom and strength who will bring you more fame than any son could."

Saying this, the Goddess vanished.

After nine months, the queen gave birth to a beautiful baby girl. She was the most wonderful child imaginable with lustrous black hair and skin like golden sunshine. The king was overjoyed and said, "She will be named Savitri, in honour of the Goddess."

Years passed and Savitri grew into an exceptionally beautiful woman. She was not only beautiful but also wise and noble. The fame of Savitri's beauty spread far and wide. Many princes and kings came to ask Savitri's hand in marriage. But Savitri refused to marry anyone of them.

Savitri's father, the king was very distressed by her refusal and said, "Savitri, many kings and princes have come to seek your hand in marriage but you

have said, "no" to everyone. Is there anyone you wish to marry?"

Savitri said politely, "Father, I have not yet found the man I wish to marry. Let me go out in the world and search for my husband. When I find the man I can marry, I will come back to you."

"Do as you please, daughter. But choose well and bring no shame upon our name," the king said.

Princess Savitri, accompanied by her father's trusted advisors and warriors travelled across many kingdoms to find her right match. She met many kings and princes but no one she wanted to marry. After many days of travelling, Savitri got tired of her search and decided to return home. As they were returning, Savitri and her companions came across a thick forest.

The forest was lush green and had many beautiful flowers. Savitri got down from her chariot and started walking through the forest. In the forest, she saw a handsome young man carrying a bundle of wood on his back. Although, he was dressed in simple clothes but he walked like a king and his face had a serene beauty no hardship could spoil. Savitri went back to her chariot and told her advisor to find out about the young man.

After sometime, the old advisor came and told Savitri what he had discovered about the young man.

"O princes, the young man's name is Satyavan. He is the son of the blind king Dyumatsena."

"If he is a prince," asked Savitri, "what is he doing in the forest?"

"His is a sad story. A couple of years after Satyavan was born, the king went blind and his kingdom was taken over by his enemies. The blind king, the queen and their son were forced to live in the forest, suffering hardship and poverty. The prince looks after his parents with utmost care and love. He chops wood, sells it in the countryside and with the money he gets food for his parents. He shares great understanding and love with his parents and even though they have no luxuries, they are very happy."

When Savitri heard all this, she knew her search had ended.

"That is all I need to know about him," Savitri said to the advisor. Savitri returned to her father's kingdom to tell her father about the man she had decided to marry.

"Father," said Savitri, "I have found the man I want to marry." The king was happy on hearing this but his joy soon disappeared when he came to know that his daughter had decided to marry a penniless prince. A wise brahmin was visiting the king's court and heard Savitri's words. "O King," said the brahmin, "I know the young prince. His name is Satyavan. He is as noble as he is handsome and his

gracious ways are known throughout the countryside."

The king felt a little relieved on hearing this but what the brahmin said next made the king unhappy again.

"But there is a problem," said the brahmin. "Satyavan has a curse laid upon him. He is to die within a year."

The king became terrified on hearing this and said, "Choose someone else, my child. You cannot marry this prince who is fated to die in a year."

But Savitri insisted on marrying Satyavan, "I love Satyavan and I will marry him, no matter what. I would rather be his widow than someone else's wife."

The poor king had no choice but to succumb to Savitri's wish. With a heavy heart, the king gave his consent for the marriage.

The marriage of Savitri and Satyavan was a grand affair. The whole palace was covered with white jasmine flowers and lamps which twinkled like little stars. There was a great feast after the wedding. After the celebration was over, Savitri removed her luxurious wedding clothes and jewellery and changed into a simple cotton sari. Then, Savitri and Satyavan went to their simple hut in the forest.

Savitri took over Satyavan's duties and took great care of the blind king and the queen. In return, she received their blessings and Satyavan's unlimited affection. For a whole year, Savitri and Satyavan lived happily sharing great love and understanding.

Savitri went about doing her duties cheerfully, hiding the dreadful secret about her husband in her heart. With each passing day, she saw death coming nearer to her husband, but she did not let Satyavan or his parents know about this great sorrow. On the last day of Satyavan's life, Savitri decided to accompany her husband into the forest.

"Please, dear husband," requested Savitri, "I want to accompany you to the forest". Satyavan did not want to turn down Savitri's request as she seldom asked for anything.

Savitri and Satyavan walked through the forest where birds were singing and peacocks were dancing. The trees were covered with lush green leaves and flowers bloomed all around. But all this beauty went unnoticed by Savitri. Her only thoughts were about her husband and his impending death.

"Savitri," said Satyavan, "why don't you rest under the tree while I chop some wood?" Satyavan started cutting the tree while Savitri rested. While Satyavan was cutting the tree, he felt a sudden pain in his limbs and his axe dropped from his hands.

"I am feeling very tired," said Satyavan. "Savitri, let me rest my head for a while in your lap."

Savitri immediately came and put her husband's head in her lap while his body rested on earth. "Death is calling my lord," thought Savitri as she looked at Satyavan, her eyes gazing at him as if taking a last look of his live form.

Suddenly, the whole forest plunged in darkness. The air was shimmering and Savitri could see a man glowing in the dark. He was as tall as the giant trees and glowed like the sun. He was wearing a golden crown and held a noose in his hand. Savitri knew that this man had come to take her husband's soul. Savitri gently placed Satyavan's head on the grass and rose, bowing with palms folded.

"The God of Death has sent you," Savitri asked shaking with fright.

"I am Yamaraj himself, the God of Death. I have come to take your husband's soul," Yamaraj said in a serious tone.

"You have come yourself," asked Savitri, a little surprised. "O Great God, don't you usually send your messengers for this purpose."

"Your husband Satyavan was a noble man. When a high souled person like him dies, I come myself to take his soul. It would be an insult to send anyone else," Yamaraj said.

Yamaraj looked at Satyavan's body and using his noose took away his soul. Satyavan's tiny soul, less than the size of a thumb, left his body and went to the God. Having taken the soul, Yamaraj turned and walked away. But he had hardly taken a few steps, when he realized Savitri was following him.

"You cannot go where I am going, Savitri," Yamaraj said politely, "Go back and arrange your husband's funeral."

"It is my duty to follow my husband," said Savitri. "You have taken his soul and so I must follow you."

Yamaraj was pleased with Savitri's answer and granted her a boon.

"Ask for anything except your husband's life and I shall grant it," said Yamaraj.

"Grant that Satyavan's father, the blind king, may see again," Savitri said instantly.

"Your wish is granted," said Yamaraj and started walking again. But Savitri still followed him.

"Go back, Savitri," said Yamaraj firmly, "you cannot follow me."

But Savitri insisted that she would follow him. Yamaraj granted Savitri another boon in the hope that after this Savitri would not follow him.

"Anything except your husband's life," Yamaraj repeated.

"Grant that my husband's father regain his kingdom," said Savitri.

Yamaraj fulfilled that wish too and started walking again. But again, he heard Savitri's footsteps following him.

"I am granting you another boon," said Yamaraj, "and nothing after that."

"Grant that I may have a hundred sons," said Savitri.

"So be it," said Yamaraj. "Now you must go back."

But Savitri followed him and the God turned around and said irritably. "I have granted all that you have asked for. Now why are you following me?"

Savitri answered with deceptive meekness, "O God, I do not want to sound rude, but how can I have a hundred sons without my husband. And if I don't have sons then your words will be a lie."

Yamaraj was stunned for a moment on hearing these words.

Then, he laughed aloud and said, "You are an extraordinary woman of great wisdom. Your courage and presence of mind has made you achieve the impossible. Satyavan will be a great king and live for several hundred years," Yamaraj untied his shining noose and released Satyavan's soul. Then he disappeared.

Savitri ran back to where Satyavan's body lay. Tears of joy fell from Savitri eyes as she saw her husband opening his eyes. Satyavan looked at Savitri and then looked around as if he had woken up from deep sleep.

"I had a strange dream, Savitri," said Satyavan. " I dreamt about a giant man holding a noose taking me with him. But suddenly he disappeared and I woke up."

"That was no dream," said Savitri, "That was Yamaraj, who had come to take your soul." Savitri briefly narrated the whole story to Satyavan.

"I am the luckiest man in the world to have a wife like you," said Satyavan feeling proud of his wife. "No man will ever have such a great wife."

All that Yamaraj had said came true. The blind king regained his eyesight and kingdom. After his death, Satyavan became the king. Savitri and Satyavan lived happily for several years and as Yamaraj had promised, they had a hundred sons.

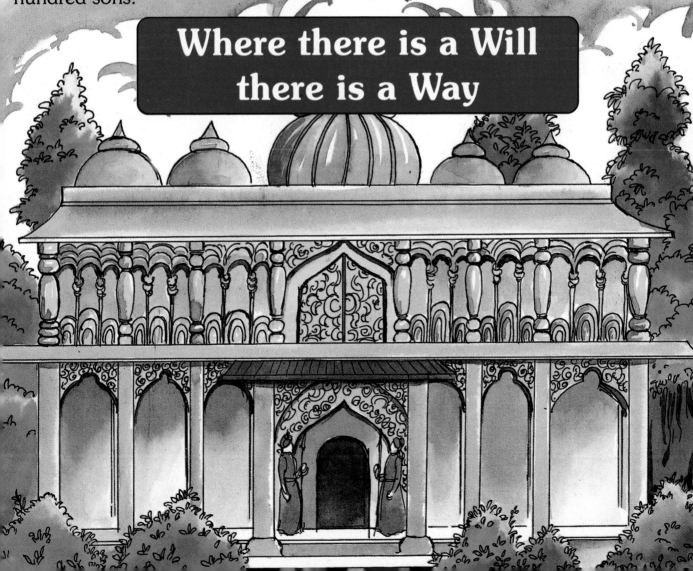

Where there is a Will there is a Way

THE BIRTH OF KARNA

King Shurasena had many children. On the other hand, his cousin king Kuntibhoja was childless. Shurasena, out of compassion, gave his daughter to Kuntibhoja. The child grew into a beautiful young girl and came to be known as Kunti.

One day, sage Durvasa visited king Kuntibhoja. Sage Durvasa was feared by everyone for his great powers and extremely short temper. When the tall, fierce eyed sage entered the court, followed by his disciples all, including the

king rose and bowed low with their hands bent and palms folded.

"O great sage, we are most fortunate to have you here," said king Kuntibhoja, a little scared.

Durvasa nodded and said, "I will stay in your palace for sometime. I want to remind you that I do not want to be disturbed and want prompt and quick service day or night. I hope my staying here would not cause you any trouble."

"Of course not, great sage. My humble abode will become auspicious with your presence," said the king.

"Good, now I am going for a bath," announced Durvasa. As soon as Durvasa left with his disciples, the king rushed to his daughter Kunti.

"What is the matter, father? Why are you looking so frightened?" asked Kunti.

"Sage Durvasa is here with his disciples and he plans to stay here for sometime," answered the king.

"Why should that be a problem? We have had sages and rishis as guests all the time," said Kunti.

"You don't understand, my child," cried out the king. "Durvasa is not an ordinary sage. He has great powers and a curse from him can destroy the world, forget my kingdom. He is extremely short tempered and if anything annoys him, he is very quick with his curses. I want you to take care of him personally. Make sure he gets anything he asks for, whenever he wants, however he wants. Do not argue or ask questions and make no complaints."

"Do not worry, father. I will take good care of sage Durvasa," Kunti answered confidently.

The king felt relieved and left.

For one whole year, Kunti served Durvasa with complete devotion. Often Durvasa ordered food in the middle of the night and Kunti went herself to serve him. The whimsical sage would ask for fruit that was out of season and food that was unavailable but Kunti tried her best to satisfy him. Kunti remained patient and uncomplaining all throughout the year.

At the end of one year, Durvasa said to Kunti, "I am very pleased with you, child. You deserve a boon for your hard work and patience."

"That you are pleased is a reward in itself," answered Kunti humbly.

"Well, since you won't ask, it seems I must give you something. I will teach you a mantra that will give you sons by the Gods. If you call upon any god by repeating this mantra, he will appear before you and bless you with a son equal to him in glory," Durvasa said proudly.

Durvasa taught the mantra to Kunti and left the palace with his disciples, much to everyone's relief.

Kunti was excited by the new *mantra* learnt by her and was curious to try it out. One day, out of curiosity, she decided to recite the *mantra* and see if it really worked.

Kunti called upon the Sun God by repeating the *mantra*. The next moment, Kunti's room was lit with a dazzling light. The light was so bright that Kunti had to shut her eyes. When she opened her eyes, slowly again, she saw Surya or the Sun God standing before her.

"I will give you the son you prayed for," said the Sun God.

Kunti trembled with fear on hearing this and said, "I don't want a son. I only recited the *mantra* to see if it worked."

But Surya told her that he was bound by the *mantra* and would give her a son.

"But I am not even married," argued Kunti.

"The *mantra* binds me and a son you shall have," declared Surya in a serious tone.

Nine months later, Kunti gave birth to a beautiful baby boy. The child was beautiful and bright, as bright as Surya himself. The child was born with a golden armour attached to his torso like a second skin. He also wore golden earrings that had a reddish glow.

Kunti was terrified. She knew her father and those around her would be angry with her. She hugged the child and wept bitterly.

"I can't keep you, my son, I can't," Kunti cried.

Then, in the dead of the night, she placed the baby in a silk lined basket and hurried out of the palace. She went to a river and gently placed the basket on the waves of the river water. Tears flowed down Kunti's cheeks as she saw her baby being carried away with the waves. Then, she hurried back to the palace.

But, the baby whom Kunti had cruelly abandoned, was not destined to die. A charioteer found the baby and took it home. The child was named Karna, the one with earrings.

Karna grew up and became an expert archer. He was one of the greatest warriors in the Mahabharata.

Look Before You Leap

THE MONKEY'S ADVICE

Once upon a time, there lived a king who had many monkeys. He kept these monkeys to entertain his son. The monkeys were fed good food and enjoyed the comforts of the palace.

Besides the monkeys, a herd of sheep was also kept at the palace grounds. One of the sheep was always running into the royal kitchen to nibble at whatever he could find. This always angered the cooks and the cooks would often throw whatever they could lay their hands on at the sheep, to chase him away.

A wise, old monkey had watched this happen many times. He called all the monkeys and said to them, "This sheep is going to get us all killed one day. The cooks become very angry when the sheep enters the kitchen. Suppose, one day they throw a lighted wood at the sheep. Then, the sheep's thick wool will catch fire. To save himself, the sheep will run into the stables near the kitchen.

When the sheep rolls on the hay to put off the fire, the hay will catch fire and burn the whole stable. The horses will get burnt and the doctors would say that the best cure for burns of horses is monkey fat. Then, the king will order to kill all the monkeys to provide that fat. Let us get out of here before we are all killed."

The other monkeys ignored the advice of the wise monkey and laughed at him. They said, "You are old and think only of such silly things. Why should we listen to your silly advice and leave all these comforts and good food. We do not want to live a tough life in the forest. We are happy staying here."

The old monkey became sad on hearing this.

"You are free to do whatever you choose," said the old monkey. "But I cannot stay here and see you all dying. I am leaving for the forest." Saying this, the old monkey left the palace.

After a few days, the sheep again ran into the royal kitchen. This time, one of the cooks threw a lighted wood at the sheep.

When his wool caught fire, the sheep ran into the stables where the hay caught fire. Soon, the whole stable was burning. In this fire, many horses died and many horses were severely burnt.

When the king received the news, he was very sad. He called all the doctors for their advice. The doctors said, "The only cure for these burns is monkey fat. Applying monkey fat to the burnt areas will relieve the pain."

Immediately, the king ordered that all the monkeys be killed and their fat collected. One by one, all the monkeys were killed.

Never Ignore a Friend's Advice

REVENGE OF THE MONKEY

The old monkey heard the sad news of his friends' (other monkeys) death. He was very grieved. He vowed to take revenge and teach the king a lesson. The monkey was lost in his thoughts when he came across a river. He decided to drink water.

But, as he went close to the river he noticed footsteps leading into the river but none coming out.

"Surely, there lives a beast in the river who eats anyone who enters the lake," the monkey thought.

So, the monkey took a lotus stalk, dipped it into the river and sucked water through it.

Just then, a vicious looking beast came out from the middle of the river.

"You are a very clever monkey," said the beast. "I eat anyone who enters the river. You are intelligent, I like you. What can I do for you?"

"How many men can you eat at a time," asked the monkey.

"I can eat several thousands but only if, they are in water. I have no strength on land," answered the beast.

The beast was wearing a beautiful diamond necklace around his neck. The monkey saw it and said, "Lend me your necklace. I will take it and show it to the king. That will make him greedy. Then, I will lead the king and his army to you. You can eat them all."

The beast gave the necklace to the monkey. Wearing it around his neck, the monkey went to the king's palace. When the king's soldiers saw the monkey wearing the necklace, they were amazed. They took the monkey to their king.

"From where did you get that necklace?" questioned the king.

"O king," said the monkey, "not far from here, there is a river. If anyone enters it, he comes out wearing a diamond necklace."

"Are you speaking the truth," asked the king excitedly.

"Yes! You can see yourself, the diamond necklace I am wearing."

"I believe you," said the king. "I will lead my army to the river and then I will have thousands of diamond necklaces."

"Show us that river," the king ordered the monkey.

The monkey led the king with his army to the river where the beast lived.

As soon as they reached the river, the king's soldiers dived into the river.

"My soldiers will soon be back with the necklaces," thought the greedy king.

The king waited for a long time but none of his soldiers came out of the river.

"Why are the soldiers taking so much time?" the king asked the monkey.

The monkey quickly climbed up the branch of a tall tree and replied, "Foolish king, you have been blinded by greed. Your soldiers will never return as they have been eaten up by a beast who lives in the river. When you killed my friends, I had vowed to take revenge. Now all your soldiers are dead. I spared you because you are a king. I have taken my revenge."

The king was filled with sorrow on hearing these words. With a heavy heart, he returned alone to his palace.

Greed Always Leads to Sorrow

BIRBAL'S JUSTICE

In a small village in Agra, lived a poor farmer. He worked very hard and always managed to support and feed his family. The farmer was very poor, but still he never borrowed money from anyone. The farmer was very proud of this fact and would often tell his wife, "We must never borrow money from anyone, last of all from the moneylender. If ever we fall into his clutches, we will be ruined."

The fear of borrowing money was so deep rooted in the farmer that one night he had a dream about it. The farmer dreamt that he had borrowed five hundred gold coins from the moneylender. He suddenly woke up and started shouting, "Oh! How will I ever return the five hundred gold coins that I borrowed?"

The noise woke up his wife. The farmer told his wife about his dream. The wife said, "Why worry so much? It is only a dream."

Then, the farmer and his wife went back to sleep. The next morning, the farmer's wife told her friends about her husband's dream. Her friends found the story strange and amusing. Soon, the story spread throughout the village and reached the moneylender's ears. On hearing the story, the greedy moneylender had an evil thought. In the evening, he went to meet the farmer.

"What brings you here, Lalaji?" asked the farmer.

"I have come to collect my money, five hundred gold coins," said the moneylender.

"Five hundred gold coins," stammered the farmer. "It was only a dream. I never actually took the money," the farmer cried out.

"Money is money," answered the moneylender. "I am not telling you to return all my money at once. You can pay me five gold coins a month with interest." Saying this, the moneylender went away.

The poor farmer became very sad. The farmer narrated the whole story to his wife. After thinking for a while, the wife said, "Go and meet Birbal. He is very wise and will surely help us." The farmer went to meet Birbal.

Birbal listened to the farmer's story and said, "Do not worry! I know how to handle this. Tell the moneylender to meet me at my house tomorrow morning. I will settle his debt."

The farmer gave Birbal's message to the moneylender. The next morning, the moneylender went to Birbal's house. When Birbal saw the moneylender, he said, "Ah, so you have come to collect your debt."

The moneylender said yes, nodding his head.

"Very fine," said Birbal, "come with me."

Birbal led the moneylender to a room. In the room, there was a table with a pile of gold coins on it. Behind the coins there was a mirror in which the reflection of the gold coins could be seen.

The moneylender looked greedily at the gold coins and started smiling. The mirror behind the coins made the pile look twice as big and more glittering.

"So, Lalaji," said Birbal, "I have heard this farmer borrowed five hundred gold coins in his dream."

"Very true, sir," answered the moneylender not taking his eyes off the pile of gold coins.

"Well," said Birbal, "there are five hundred gold coins on the table. You may take the five hundred gold coins you see in the mirror."

The moneylender was happy to hear Birbal's words and started greedily collecting the coins.

"Stop," shouted Birbal. "Keep those coins back. I said you could take the coins you see in the mirror, not the coins lying on the table."

"But sir," replied the moneylender, "how can I get the coins I see in the mirror. Those coins are nothing but the reflection of the coins on the table."

"Precisely, Lalaji," answered Birbal, "then how can the farmer borrow money in his dream which is nothing but the reflection of his own thoughts."

The moneylender realized that he had met his match. The moneylender hung down his head in shame and quietly left.

Tit for Tat

KING SHIBI - THE GREATEST GIVER

God Brahma, the creator of the universe, was having a discussion with the other Gods.

"Who is the most generous human being on earth?" asked Brahma.

"King Shibi, of course," said the God of Fire, Agni. "He is the greatest giver."

"His fame has reached me too, God Agni," said Brahma, "but I want to test his generosity."

So, Brahma sent God Agni and God Indra on earth to test king Shibi.

One day, when king Shibi was in his court, a dove flew in from the window. The dove went straight to the king and said, "Please protect me, great king. My enemy is following me. He will kill me."

The king looked at the bird and said, "You need not be afraid. You have taken refuge here and it is my duty to protect you."

Just then, a huge hawk, who had been chasing the dove, arrived.

"O king, hand over that dove to me. That is my lawful prey. I have won it after hard labour," said the hawk.

"I have promised to protect this dove," said king Shibi.

"You have no right to the take away what belongs to me. You may interfere in the case of human beings but birds are free in the sky. I am hungry and I need my food," said the hawk.

"To satisfy your hunger, I shall arrange for the meat of a whole bull or deer. You can have that. It will certainly be better than the flesh of this small dove," answered the king.

"I do not like the flesh of bulls or deers. I only relish the taste of doves," said the hawk.

"But there must be something else that you like. Tell me, what else you like and I shall get it," said the king.

"In that case, I would like to taste your flesh. Give me flesh from your body equal in weight to the weight of the dove," the hawk said.

"What you say shall be done," announced the king.

King Shibi ordered a pair of scales and a sharp knife to be brought to him. He put the dove on one side of the scale and started cutting his own flesh to weigh it against the dove.

Everyone in the court was shocked on seeing this. The queen wanted the king to stop but the king told her to be patient.

King Shibi said, "I am only doing my duty. Even if one has to give up one's life in the pursuit of duty, one should not back off."

The king cut pieces of flesh from his arms and thighs, filling the scale but the bird weighed heavier. More and more flesh was cut from the king's body and the bones underneath the flesh became visible. But still, the scale tilted in favour of the bird and the bird was heavier.

Everyone including the king was surprised with these happenings. At last, the king himself sat on the scale and the scale balanced. The king asked the hawk to eat him up.

At that moment, the hawk and the dove disappeared. In their place, there appeared God Indra and God Agni.

"For this generous act," said the Gods, "you will be known as one of the greatest givers of all times. Your fame will spread far and wide and you shall be remembered as long as the world lasts. The wounds on your body will heal immediately without leaving a scar."

After blessing the king, the Gods vanished and the king's body recovered the flesh that was cut.

Generosity is Always Rewarded

PIGEONS AND THE HUNTER

A flock of pigeons was searching for food. They had been flying for a long time but still could not find any food. Then, suddenly, the leader of the pigeons said, "I can see some food down on the ground." The pigeons looked down and found some rice scattered on the ground, under a big tree.

"Let us go and eat," said the leader. The pigeons landed on the ground and started eating the rice. But then, suddenly, a big net fell over them and they were trapped.

"We are caught in a trap," cried the leader.

"I see a hunter coming towards us," said another pigeon. "He is carrying a big axe."

"We must do something before this hunter kills us," said the leader of the pigeons.

"You are our leader," cried the pigeons, "Tell us how we can save ourselves."

"We must act together," said the leader. "We shall all fly up, carrying the net with us. Remember, united we stand, divided we fall." Each pigeon picked up the net with his beak and then together, they all flew up carrying the net with them.

The hunter was amazed to see his catch getting away. "How can they fly with the net?" said the hunter. "I cannot let them get away. I will run after them. These birds will soon get tired of carrying the net and fall on the ground.

Then I will catch them." The hunter ran after the pigeons hoping the net and the pigeons would soon fall down. But the united pigeons were determined to get away. They flew high over the mountains and went far away. The hunter soon grew tired of following them and gave up the chase.

The leader of the pigeons saw that the hunter was no longer after them and said, "The hunter has given up the chase. Now, we must fly to the city. There lives my friend, the mouse. He will cut the net with his teeth and set us free."

Soon, the pigeons reached the city where the mouse lived. The mouse saw the pigeons trapped in the net and became surprised. The leader of the pigeons told his friend, the mouse, the whole story.

"You are the only one who can help us," said the leader. "Cut the net with your teeth and set us free."

The mouse started cutting the net and one by one all the pigeons were set free.

The pigeons thanked the mouse for saving them and with a loud flapping of wings happily flew away in the air.

Unity is Strength

THE FOOLISH CROCODILE

A monkey lived on an apple tree by the side of a river. The tree had lots of apples and the monkey loved eating apples.

One day the monkey saw a crocodile coming out of the river. "Why are you here?" the monkey asked the crocodile.

The crocodile looked at the monkey and said, "I am searching for food."

"You want food. I have lots of apples!" Saying this, the monkey threw some apples down for the crocodile.

The crocodile liked the apples very much. "Thank you," said the crocodile. "Can I come again tomorrow for more apples."

"Yes, you can," replied the monkey. The crocodile went home happily.

The next day the crocodile came again. The monkey gave him more apples. The crocodile came everyday and the two spent a lot of time talking to each other. Eventually, the two became friends.

One day the monkey asked the crocodile where he lived. "I live on the other side of the river with my wife," answered the crocodile.

"Oh, so you have a wife," said the monkey, "Take some apples for her also."

The crocodile took the apples and went home. His wife tasted the apples and said, "These apples are delicious. Can you get them for me everyday." The crocodile said yes he would. Everyday, the monkey gave apples for the crocodile's wife. One day, his wife asked, "Where do you get these apples from?"

The crocodile told her about his friend the monkey, who lived on the apple tree.

Hearing this, the crocodile's wife thought, "This monkey eats only sweet apples so his flesh must be sweet too. I must get this monkey here and eat him up"

Then, she told her husband, "Your friend has given us so many gifts. Why don't you invite him home for dinner? I would like to meet him" But the crocodile refused to do so as he did not trust his wife.

With each passing day, the crocodile's wife became more eager to eat the monkey's flesh. Then, she thought of a plan to fulfil her craving.

One day, when the crocodile came home, his wife pretended to be very ill. The crocodile became worried and asked his wife what could he do for her.

"I am very ill. The doctor has said that the only way for me to get well is to eat a monkey's heart. You must get your friend's heart if you want me to get well."

"No, I cannot do that. I cannot harm my friend," said the crocodile.

"Then you don't want me to get well. You don't love me. You only love your friend" said his wife.

"But how can I harm my only friend?" asked the crocodile sadly.

"If you don't get me the monkey, I will kill myself. When you come back tomorrow, you will find me dead," his wife said angrily.

The crocodile became very sad. He did not want to hurt his friend but at the same time he felt it was his duty to take care of his wife. He decided to get the monkey and save his wife's life.

The next day, the crocodile went to the monkey and said, "I want to invite you home. My wife wants to meet you."

"I too would like to meet her," said the monkey, "But you live on the other side of the river. How will I get there?"

"You can sit on my back while I swim across the river," answered the crocodile.

The monkey happily agreed and sat on the crocodile's back. The crocodile started swimming across the river with the monkey on his back. When they were in the middle of the river, the crocodile began to sink.

"What are you doing," asked the frightened monkey. "I will drown if you go down any further."

"I want to drown you," said the crocodile, "I have to kill you."

"You want to kill me. You are my friend, why do you want to kill me?" asked the monkey in surprise.

The crocodile told him that his wife was ill and the only way to save her was to make her eat a monkey's heart. "You are the only monkey I know. So I will kill you and give her your heart."

The monkey got scared on hearing this. But then he thought for a while and said, "My friend, why didn't you tell me before? If my heart can save your wife then I would be most happy to give it to you. But I don't have it now. I keep my heart in a hole on the tree."

"Oh, then what do we do now?" asked the crocodile.

"Let us not waste time," said the monkey. "Let us go back at once and get the heart."

The crocodile turned back and swam as fast as he could. When they reached the tree, the monkey jumped off the crocodile's back and quickly climbed up the tree. He sat on a high branch and said to the crocodile, "Now go back alone to your evil wife and tell her that her husband is a fool."

A Foolish Friend is More Dangerous than a Clever Enemy

VISHWAMITRA

Long, long ago, there was a powerful king named Vishwamitra. He ruled over a vast kingdom. Vishwamitra was very fond of hunting. One day, he went into the jungles with his several soldiers. He spent all day hunting various animals.

In the evening, Vishwamitra decided to return to his palace. The journey to the palace was a long one. Vishwamitra and his soldiers were tired and hungry.

"Look around," said Vishwamitra to his soldiers. "See, if we can find some water and food." They travelled for a while and came across a hermitage (hut of a sage).

"Maybe we can find something here," thought Vishwamitra.

The king went inside the hut to meet the sage (*saadhu*). The sage in the hut was none other than the great Vasishta, one of the greatest saints and teachers of the world. But the king thought him to be an ordinary sage.

"Perhaps, you can help us find some water to drink," said the king feeling doubtful.

"You all must be hungry too," said the sage. "I shall arrange some food also!" Soon, Vasishta produced a large quantity of milk enough for the king and his soldiers. Afterwards, the king and his soldiers were given the best food they had ever tasted.

Vishwamitra was completely amazed with these happenings.

"How could the sage do all this in such a short time? There is nobody to help him either," thought Vishwamitra. Vishwamitra could see no human except only a cow and her calf at the hermitage.

King Vishwamitra thanked the sage for his hospitality and decided to continue his journey.

"It is already late in the evening, your majesty," said the sage. "I would suggest you and your soldiers should stay here tonight. Tomorrow early morning, you can resume your journey to the palace."

Vishwamitra could see no place or beds to sleep for so many people. But he did not want to embarrass his kind host.

"Thank you," said Vishwamitra, "but we must leave now."

"Please don't worry," said Vasishta. "There is no problem of beds. I have enough for all of you."

Vishwamitra was further taken aback. But this aroused his curiosity and he wanted to see from where would Vasishta arrange all this.

In a few minutes, Vasishta produced the most comfortable beds for his guests. Vishwamitra was too tired and without questioning this miracle, fell asleep.

The next morning Vishwamitra went to Vasishta and said, "Can I ask you a question?"

"Yes, your majesty," said Vasishta.

"You live alone in this hermitage. There is nobody to help you. Then how do you produce all these luxurious things. I am amazed seeing this miracle."

"O king, I do not perform any miracle. You see that cow?"

"Yes, I do," said Vishwamitra, "That is a beautiful cow."

"Well, that she is," replied Vasishta, "but she is not an ordinary cow. She is Nandini, daughter of Kamdhenu. She can give anything one asks of her."

Vishwamitra was amazed on hearing this.

"If this is true," thought Vishwamitra, "this cow does not belong here. She should be in my palace."

"O holy sage," said Vishwamitra, "why is such a wonderful cow staying in your lonely hermitage? She should be with the king. You are a saint, you don't need Nandini. Give her to me."

"I cannot give her away like that," answered Vasishta. "She is here to look after my needs."

"I will give you a thousand cows, if you give me Nandini," said Vishwamitra.

"What will I do with a thousand cows? I am not a cowherd to look after a thousand cows," replied Vasishta.

"If Nandini is with me the whole world will benefit from her. She is being wasted here," argued Vishwamitra.

"I am sorry," said Vasishta, "but you cannot have Nandini. She belongs here and you cannot have her."

Vasishta's reply annoyed Vishwamitra and he said, "As king Vishwamitra I demand the cow. You have to obey your king's order. But I shall be kind to you. In return of Nandini, I shall give you anything you desire."

"I do not want anything," answered Vasishta, "and let me tell you king, you cannot take away Nandini by force."

"We will see that," answered Vishwamitra arrogantly. "Take that cow and follow me to the palace," Vishwamitra said to his soldiers.

Two of Vishwamitra's soldiers untied Nandini and tried to take her along with them. But Nandini did not want to go with them. Nandini broke loose and started running away. The soldiers tried to stop her but were not successful. The soldiers then untied the calf and started to walk away, hoping the cow would follow them. When Nandini saw this, she became furious and charged the soldier with such force that they had to run to save their lives.

"I am going back, now," said Vishwamitra, "but I will come again to take Nandini." Vishwamitra returned to his palace feeling humiliated.

But Vishwamitra was not the one to take humiliation lying down. He went back to Vasishta's hermitage with a huge army.

"Vasishta," said Vishwamitra, "before my army destroys your hermitage and takes away Nandini, I give you one last chance to peacefully hand over Nandini to me."

"I will never give Nandini to you," replied Vasishta. Then, Vasishta requested Nandini to produce a huge army of soldiers. Nandini granted the request and a large army appeared there.

Vishwamitra was amazed to see this miracle but this did not deter him. He ordered his army to attack Vasishta. A fierce battle was fought between the two armies in which Vishwamitra's army was completely defeated.

Vishwamitra accepted defeat and said, "Vasishta you have defeated me. You have greater powers than me. But do not think I will sit idle. I will do anything and everything to attain greater powers than you. And then we shall meet again."

Vishwamitra returned to his palace. He immediately gave up his wealth and luxurious lifestyle and went to the deepest jungles to meditate. He meditated very hard, praying for many years and then attained a position equal to Vasishta.

Pride Leads to Downfall

THE JUDGE

A partridge lived in her nest under a large banyan tree. She had been living there for many years.

One day, the partridge left her nest to search for food. She travelled for a long time but could not find any food. Finally, she saw a corn field. The corn was fully ripe and the partridge liked ripe corn. She ate as much corn as she liked and then fell asleep. She did not go home that day. She liked being in the corn field so much that for many days she happily lived in the corn field.

Meanwhile, a rabbit saw the partridge's empty nest. "What a cosy nest," the rabbit said. "Nobody lives here, I will make it my house."

So, the rabbit started living in the partridge's nest. After a few days, the patridge returned home. When she saw the rabbit in her nest, she was very angry.

"What are you doing here?" the partridge said angrily. "This is my house."

"Your house," shouted the rabbit. "I found this house empty. Nobody was living here. It is my house now. I have been living here for many days."

"You cannot stay here," said the partridge. "I built this house. I have always been living here. If you don't believe me, you can ask the neighbours."

"I don't need to ask anybody," replied the rabbit. "A house belongs to the one who lives in it. I am living in it and so it is my house now."

The partridge said, "I only went away for a few days and you have occupied my house. This is not correct. Please leave my house."

But the rabbit was not ready to leave. "I will stay where I am. If anyone will leave, it is you," shouted the rabbit.

The quarrel between the rabbit and the partridge went for a long time. Many animals and birds gathered around them and listened to their arguments. But nobody could say to whom the house belonged.

One of the animals said, "Why don't you find someone who can be the judge. Take your dispute to him and let him decide to whom the house belongs."

The partridge and the rabbit agreed and went in search for a judge. It was not easy to find a good judge. They walked for many miles and at last they came across a big cat.

The rabbit and the partridge saw the cat and got afraid. They knew that a cat was their natural enemy and were afraid to go near him.

The cat saw the rabbit and the partridge. Immediately, he held up a string of prayer beads, closed his eyes and prayed at the top of his voice.

The partridge and the rabbit were surprised to see a holy cat.

"We can ask this cat to be the judge," said the rabbit.

"Yes, but we must be careful. A cat can be very dangerous," said the partridge.

After a few minutes, the cat opened his eyes.

"O holy cat," said the partridge, "a little argument has arisen between this rabbit and me. Please listen to our dispute and decide who is right. You may punish whoever you find is in the wrong."

The cat said, "Do not say such a thing, my friend. I cannot think of harming anyone. Let god punish those who harm others. I will listen to both of you and then take my decision."

The partridge said, "I went away for a few days and this rabbit started living in my house."

"My house, my house!" shouted the rabbit.

"Please, be calm. Let me listen to the partridge and then you tell me your story," said the cat.

After the partridge had finished, the rabbit said what he had to say.

The cat was silent for a few moments. Then he said, "I am old now and cannot see or hear well. I have not understood your case. Come closer and tell me all over again."

The partridge and the rabbit were no longer afraid of the cat. They trusted him and moved closer to him. As soon as they came close, the cat pounced on them. He killed both the partridge and the rabbit with his claws and ate them up.

When Two People Quarrel-
a Third Person Gains

STORK AND THE CRAB

Once upon a time, there was a stork which lived by the side of a tank. The stork was happy as the tank had plenty of fish and he had enough to eat.

Many years passed and the stork grew old and weak. Now, he found it difficult to catch fish and sometimes, he even had to sleep hungry.

The stork thought, "Now I am not able to catch all the fish I want. If things go like this, then I would soon die of starvation. I must think of a plan to satisfy my hunger."

The next day, the stork stood by the side of the tank, looking sad. He did not even try to catch the fish which went past him.

The fish, the frogs and the crabs saw the stork like this and wondered what had happened to him. A big crab went upto him and asked, "Why are you so sad? You are not even trying to catch the fish. Why are you not taking your food?"

The stork replied sadly, "I have spent all my life by the side of this tank. All these years, I have been very happy. But, now, things will change. All the fish in the tank will soon die and I won't be left with any food."

"But, why?" asked the crab.

The stork said, "I heard some people say that this tank will be soon filled with earth and crops will be grown over it. Then, all the fish will die."

The fish, the crabs and the frogs heard what the stork had said and became scared. They went to the stork and said, "Uncle, this is indeed a very bad news."

"Oh, it is," said the stork.

"Uncle, you are intelligent. Please help us save our lives," said the fish.

The stork replied, "Perhaps, I can help you. There is a bigger and deeper tank, a little further away. It cannot be filled up easily. If you want, I can take you all there."

"Please take us there," cried all the fish.

"It is a difficult job, but do not worry. I shall do my best," said the stork.

"Take me first, take me first," cried every fish in the tank.

"Please have patience," said the stork. "I can carry only a few of you at a time. I shall try to take as many trips as possible. But I am old now and would need to rest after every trip."

In a little while, the stork set out on his first trip. He carried a few fish in his beak and flew away. But he did not take them to another tank as he had promised. Instead, he took them to a big rock and ate them up. After that, he made his next trip, carrying a few more fish. Again, he took them to the rock and ate them up.

After having enough food, he rested for a while. Later, when he felt hungry again he went back to the tank to pick up some more fish. This went on for some time.

Meanwhile, the big crab in the tank also felt that he should leave the tank and save himself.

When the stork came to the tank, the crab said, "Dear Uncle, please take me with you. Save me also."

The stork was getting bored of eating fish and thought that a crab would be a nice change of taste. "Do not worry, my friend," said the stork. "I will save you. Come, I will take you to the big tank."

The stork picked up the crab and flew away.

After some time, the crab looked down to see his new home, the big tank where he was going to live, but he could not see any water anywhere. Then the stork started flying down. The crab became surprised and said, "Uncle, where is the tank. I cannot see any water anywhere."

The stork laughed and replied, "You see that big rock down there? That is the place I am taking you to. That is the place I took all the fish to."

The crab could see the rock clearly and noticed the heaps of fish bones. He knew the stork would eat him up as soon as they would land on the rock.

His life was in danger. The crab thought for a moment. Suddenly, he dug his sharp claws into the stork and pressed his neck with all his strength. The stork flapped his wings and struggled hard to get rid of the crab but the crab was holding his neck with all his strength. Soon, the stork fell to the ground.

The crab cut the head off the stork's body. Then, he returned to the tank in which he lived.

Never Trust Your Enemy

RAVAN KIDNAPS SITA

Many, many years ago, Ayodhya was ruled by a powerful king, Dashrath. Dashrath had chosen his eldest son Ram to become the king after him. But Ram's stepmother Kaikeyi wanted her son Bharat to be the king. So she used a boon granted to her by Dashrath to send Ram away to the jungles. Ram left his father's kingdom to spend 14 years in exile. He was accompanied by his loving wife, Sita and younger brother, Lakshman.

For twelve years, they wandered through the forests, saw many great sights and killed many demons and wicked people. In the thirteenth year of their

exile, they reached a place called Panchavati in the south of India. It was a beautiful place lying on the banks of the river, Godavari. The trees were laden with fruits and the air was fragrant with the smell of flowers.

Ram and Lakshman built a hut in the forest and Sita made that hut a home. Ram, Sita and Lakshman lived in peace in the forest. But the forest had its dark side. It was filled with dangerous *rakshasas* or demons. The demons were very cunning and experts at disguise. Not far from the hut of Ram, lived a demoness, Surpanakha. She was the sister of Ravan, the powerful king of Lanka. Surpanakha was roaming around in the forest when she saw Ram and wished to marry him. Using her magic, she disguised herself as a beautiful maiden and said to Ram, "I am Surpanakha, sister of Ravan, the great king of Lanka. I wish to marry you."

Ram gave her a sweet smile and answered politely, "Fair maiden, I cannot marry you as I am already married to Sita."

"That woman is not fit to be your wife. Come with me and I will get you anything you desire," Surpanakha said to Ram.

Ram was amused on hearing this and said jokingly, "Why don't you marry my brother, Lakshman?"

Surpanakha went to Lakshman but Lakshman flatly refused her proposal.

This angered Surpanakha and she assumed her true form of a demoness. She looked terrifying and Sita became afraid on seeing her.

Surpanakha looked angrily at Sita and said, "I will kill you and then Ram can marry me." Surpanakha rushed towards Sita to kill her but Lakshman immediately drew out his sword and cut her nose and ears.

Howling in agony, Surpanakha fled from there. She went to her brothers Khar and Dushan who lived in the forest not far away. When the demon brothers saw their sister with a bleeding nose and ears they became furious. They collected their army of demons and attacked the hermitage. A fierce battle was fought in which the army of the demons was completely routed. The demons fought with all their strength but were no match for the divine weapons of Ram. The brothers, Khar and Dushan were killed along with most of their soldiers and the rest fled away.

When Surpanakha heard her brothers were dead, she wanted nothing now but revenge. She flew to Lanka, which lay beyond the great ocean, to meet her brother, Ravan. When Ravan saw Surpanakha's disfigured face, he was shocked. "Who has dared to do this to you?" asked Ravan angrily.

"The banished princes of Ayodhya," Surpanakha said, stamping her foot angrily.

"I will kill them," Ravan shouted angrily.

"No," shouted Surpanakha, "I don't want you to kill them. Besides, it is very difficult to kill them. Ram and Lakshman single handedly killed your brothers, Khar and Dushan and destroyed their entire army."

Ravan was further grieved and furious to hear about the demise of his brothers. Surpanakha said to Ravan, "You should avenge your brothers' death and my insult but not by killing Ram and Lakshman. Instead, I want you take Ram's beautiful wife, Sita, away from him. Without her, Ram will die and without Ram, Lakshman will die. That is the proper way to take our revenge."

As Surpanakha told Ravan about Sita's beauty, he liked the idea of abducting Sita ever more. "Sita, the wife of Ram, is very beautiful. She would make a lovely queen for you, dear brother," said Surpanakha.

Ravan summoned his flying chariot and flew off to Panchavati. But he did not go to Ram's hut. Ravan knew that to kidnap Sita, he would need the help of Mareech, the demon magician who lived in the same forest. Mareech was a very cunning demon and could disguise himself as any man, bird or beast using his magic.

Ravan said to Mareech, "I want you to help me kidnap Sita."

"Don't commit this sin," Mareech advised, "you will be paying for it with your life. Ram will kill you."

"I do not need your advice," said the ten-headed demon king. "I am your king and you have to obey my orders, otherwise you will have to die."

Mareech thought for a while and said, "I will die either ways. It is better to die at Ram's hands, while doing my duty of serving my king."

Ravan was happy to hear this.

"I want you to take the form of a golden deer," Ravan said. "Sita will desire you and send Ram and Lakshman after you. Then, Sita will be alone in the hut and I will carry her away."

Mareech again warned Ravan of the dire consequences of this action but Ravan laughed at him. Mareech assumed the form of a golden deer and appeared before the hut of Ram. Sita saw the beautiful deer and her eyes lit up. "How beautiful you are," Sita said softly. Then, she called out to Ram. Pointing to the golden deer, Sita said to Ram, "I wish to have the skin of that golden deer."

Ram smiled and said, "A deer can never be of gold. This is unreal. Always remember, all that glitters is not gold." Lakshman also came out and saw the deer, "This deer is probably that demon Mareech in disguise," Lakshman said suspiciously. "Mareech can take any form he wants."

But Sita was much too enchanted by the deer to listen to any sensible advice. She pleaded to Ram to get her the deer, "I have never asked you for anything all these years," said Sita. "Now I ask, please get me this deer."

Ram had no choice but to do as Sita wished.

"Lakshman," said Ram, "I will go after the deer but you stay here and take care of Sita. Do not leave her alone even for a moment."

The deer ran into the forest and Ram went after it. After chasing it for a while, Ram shot an arrow which pierced the golden skin of the deer. The deer vanished and in its place lay a wounded demon. The injured demon cried out for help in Ram's voice, "O Sita! O Lakshman! Help me." The demon said these last words and died.

Sita heard the cry for help and said, "Lakshman, that is my lord Ram's voice. He is in danger. Go and help him."

"Ram would never cry for help!" said Lakshman confidently. "He is unconquerable even by the Gods. It is probably some demon trying to trick us."

"Do you think I do not know my lord's voice," shouted Sita angrily. "Go and help him."

"But I cannot leave you alone in the hut," reasoned Lakshman

Sita was much too scared for Ram's safety to listen to any reasonings. Fear and anger made Sita say nasty things to Lakshman.

"Are you not going because Ram is your stepbrother?" said Sita angrily to Lakshman. "All your love and concern for Ram is a pretence. If you do not go right away, I will kill myself."

Lakshman was deeply hurt to hear all this. He knew he had to do as Sita wished. Taking his arrow, he drew a circle around the entrance of the hut and said, "Do not step beyond this circle and no harm will come to you."

Saying this, Lakshman went in search of Ram leaving Sita alone.

All this time, Ravan was hiding behind a tree. When he saw Lakshman disappear into the forest, he said a magic *mantra* and his royal clothes and nine of his ten heads disappeared. Ravan changed his form and became a *sanyasi* (ascetic), wearing saffron clothes and wooden sandals. With a begging bowl in one hand he approached the hut.

Sita saw the gentle-faced sanyasi and rose to greet him. Staying within the safety circle she offered fruits to Ravan who was disguised as a sanyasi.

Ravan noticed the safety circle and knew that he could not kidnap Sita as long as she was inside the circle. If he wanted to kidnap her, he must make her come out of it.

Ravan said to Sita, "I am a sanyasi and cannot enter any home. I cannot accept your offer of fruits from inside the hut. If you want me to accept your offerings, you will have to come out and give them to me."

Sita did not want a Sanyasi to go without accepting food. That would be a very bad omen.

"What harm can a Sanyasi do?" thought Sita.

Thus, disregarding Lakshman's warning, she stepped across the circle, holding a basket of fruits in her hands. The moment she did this, the sanyasi disappeared and in his place stood a towering, richly dressed man, with a jewelled crown on his head.

"Who are you?" asked Sita fearing the towering demon.

"I am Ravan, the king of Lanka," Ravan answered proudly. "Come with me and become my queen. That Ram is not fit to be your husband."

Sita became furious on hearing this. "How dare you compare yourself to my Lord? How can a drop compare itself to an ocean."

But Ravan did not care for the insults. "I can toss the earth on my arms and take any form at will," Ravan boasted.

Ravan spoke of his strength and feats of war to intimidate Sita but it only made Sita more angry. Then, Ravan said, "Willing or unwilling, you have to come with me." Ravan sprang on Sita, like a tiger on its prey and seized her.

Sita cried for help, "O Ram! O Lakshman! Help me."

Ravan laughed loudly and said, "No one will come to save you. You will be my queen."

"You sinner! My lord Ram will kill you for this," Sita said angrily with tears in her eyes.

Ravan carried the crying Sita to his flying chariot. As the chariot rose into the air, Sita tried to jump out but Ravan held her tightly. The chariot flew at a very fast speed and Sita lost all hopes of being saved. She started taking off her ornaments and dropped them to the ground in the hope that they would lead Ram to her.

All that Glitters is Not Gold

After several days of search and with the help of monkey king, Sugriv, Ram and Lakshman rescued Sita and killed Ravan. Thus, Ravan was punished for his evil deed.

MONGOOSE AND THE BABY

In a village, there lived a farmer with his wife and his newly born son. Once, the farmer went to the market and saw a little mongoose. "This tiny, little mongoose will make a good pet for my son" the farmer thought. "I shall take him home."

The farmer's wife was happy to see the mongoose and liked the idea of having a pet.

After about six months, the mongoose was fully grown while the farmer's son was still a baby. The mongoose had grown up to be a beautiful animal with shining, black eyes and a long bushy tail.

One day, the farmer's wife had some work in the market. She said to her husband, "I am going to the market. The baby is sleeping. You must not leave the baby alone. I do not want our child to be alone with the mongoose. The mongoose has grown up and can harm our child."

But, the farmer said, "Please, do not worry. The mongoose loves our baby and would not harm him."

The farmer's wife went to the market. After sometime, the farmer also went out to meet his friends. Meanwhile, a snake entered the farmer's house. The snake saw the baby sleeping and went towards him. The mongoose saw the snake approaching the baby and he immediately attacked the snake to protect the baby. The snake and the mongoose fought fiercely, but, in a few minutes, the mongoose managed to kill the snake.

When the farmer's wife returned, carrying a basketful of groceries, the mongoose ran towards her to welcome her. The farmer's wife saw the paws and the face of the mongoose covered with blood. She became frightened and screamed, "Blood. Oh, you killed my son. You evil mongoose, I will kill you."

The farmer's wife, with all her strength, threw the heavy basket of groceries on the mongoose. Then, she ran straight to the baby's cradle.

She saw that the baby was fast asleep. But, on the floor, near the cradle was a dead black snake, covered with blood. Immediately, the farmer's wife realized that the mongoose had killed the snake and protected her son.

She realised her mistake, but, now it was too late.

The mongoose was already dead.

Never Act in Haste

LION AND THE SHEEP

A flock of sheep was grazing in the forest. While grazing, one of the sheep got separated from the rest of the flock.

"Oh, my friends have moved on while I was eating the grass," the sheep thought. "Now I am left alone."

Although the sheep was alone, he was not afraid. He confidently moved around in the forest.

He was a big sheep with large horns and woolly body. The wild animals of the forest saw him and said, "No doubt, this animal is very powerful. He will make a dangerous enemy. Let us stay away from him."

Soon, a lion came along and saw the sheep. He looked at the sheep and said to himself, "I have never seen such an animal. He looks so fierce and powerful.

His horns look so strong that they could even pierce an elephant's body. This animal must surely be stronger than me." Thus saying this, the lion went away. After a while, the lion again saw the sheep. The sheep was eating grass and the lion became surprised on seeing this.

"This is very strange," thought the lion. "This strong looking animal eats grass. He cannot be stronger than me as his strength must be in proportion to the food he eats. I will fight with him."

Thus, the lion attacked the sheep with all his strength. The poor sheep was no match for the powerful lion. The lion easily killed the sheep.

As the lion was eating the sheep, he thought, "I was fooled by this sheep's appearance. Looks are certainly deceptive."

Appearances are Deceptive

KRISHNA AND KALIYA

Long, long ago, the earth was suffering from the tortures of demons and sinners. So, along with Brahma, the creator of the world, Goddess Earth went to Lord Vishnu to ask for help.

Lord Vishnu said, "Do not worry, Goddess Earth. I myself shall be born on earth as a human and free you from the clutches of sinners."

Thus, Lord Vishnu came to earth being born as Krishna.

Krishna was the eighth son of Devaki and Vasudeva. The cruel king, Kansa had promised to kill every child of Devaki. So, to protect their baby, Vasudeva gave Krishna to his friend Nand Baba. Little Krishna was looked after with great love and care by Nand Baba and his wife Yashoda in Gokul.

Krishna was very active and cheerful and everyone in the village adored him, especially the girls. Every minute a new mischief occurred to him. It was his mischievous nature that made his childhood so fascinating.

Often, Krishna would steal into any house along with his friends, break the pots full of butter and curd with a rod and eat up all of it.

Everyday, the villagers complained to Yashoda about Krishna's naughty acts. Most of the times Krishna won over her mother with his sweet smile and escaped punishment. But sometimes, Yoshoda controlled her motherly affection and punished Krishna. Once, to punish Krishna for his mischief, Yashoda tied him to a massive mortar. Then, she went inside the house to do some work. Krishna sat down on his knees and caused the mortar to

tumble down so that it could roll when drawn. Then, Krishna began to crawl on his knees and the mortar started rolling.

The rolling mortar got stuck between two trees. Krishna tugged and pulled the mortar which made the trees come crashing down. Hearing the loud noise, Yashoda came out running. She untied her son and almost weeping, clasped him to her bosom. Krishna smiled as his mother doled out affection on him.

Not long after, the people of Gokul decided to leave their village and settle in Vrindavan on the banks of the river Yamuna. Krishna loved his new home. The trees in Vrindavan were lush green and the air was always cool. There was a river to swim in and wide grassy fields. Everyday, Krishna took his little calves to graze with the other cowboys.

But soon, a problem presented itself. In the river Yamuna, lived an extremely poisonous Cobra (snake), Kaliya.

This Cobra had a 101 hoods (heads) and with the poison that he spat, he had poisoned the water of the Yamuna. All the fishes, frogs and turtles in the Yamuna died because of the poisonous water. Even the cattle and people who drank the poisonous water died instantly. Clouds of gloom and fear covered Vrindavan. The people were no longer happy and children were forbidden to go near the Yamuna river, putting an end to all the merry sport in the cool waters.

Krishna decided to kill Kaliya and end the reign of terror.

One day, Krishna, while playing with his friends, purposely thew his ball into the poisonous river. Then, he jumped into the waters to get the ball. Kaliya saw Krishna and got furious. Hissing violently, it gripped Krishna in its curl. Krishna freed himself from Kaliya's grip and jumped on his hoods. Krishna began to dance on the hoods of the Cobra and at the same time began to play on his flute. He laughed as Kaliya tried to shake him off. Then, Krishna stamped his foot so hard on his hood that it got injured and blood started coming out.

The waters of Yamuna became red as Kaliya's blood mixed with the river water. Seeing the blood, the people on the bank feared the worst; Kaliya would kill Krishna. But then, they heard Kaliya's cry for forgiveness. "Spare me, please spare me." Kaliya's wives too begged Krishna for forgiveness.

"I will spare you," said Krishna, "provided you take your family and go away from here."

Kaliya promised to leave with his family and Krishna leapt off the snake's head. Kaliya left with his family as promised. He went to live in the great ocean far away and never came back to Vrindavan.

Vrindavan was once again filled with joy and happiness.